Neil Armstrong's Wind Tunnel Dream

* * *

Written by Rinda Beach

Illustrations by
Cole Roberts

BEACH GIRL PRESS/WAPAKONETA

Neil Armstrong™ Used with Permission from The Purdue Research Foundation.

Rinda Beach/Beach Girl Press
821 Glyncrest Drive, Wapakoneta, Ohio 45895

www.rindabeach.com

Publisher's Note: This is a work of fiction. Names, characters, places, and incidents are a product of the author's imagination. Locales and public names are sometimes used for atmospheric purposes. Any resemblance to actual people, living or dead, or to businesses, companies, events, institutions, or locales is completely coincidental.

Book design © 2017 BookDesignTemplates.com

Ordering Information: Special discounts are available on quantity purchases by corporations, associations, and others. For details, contact the publisher at the address above.

Neil Armstrong's Wind Tunnel Dream / Rinda Beach — First Edition

ISBN   978-1-7335892-0-8 eBook

ISBN   978-1-7335892-1-5 paperback

ISBN   978-1-7335892-2-2 hard cover

Printed in the United States of America

Table of Contents

For all dreamers, no matter your age. Live your dreams, and they can come true, just like Neil's did.

Foreward

Neil Alden Armstrong was the first man to set foot on the moon on July 20, 1969. Most people know that story, but very few know how Neil's teen-age dream to build a wind tunnel helped him walk into history.

CHAPTER 1
A Dream Begins and Grows

Planes banked and darted toward the finish line at the 1932 air races in Cleveland, Ohio.

Two-year-old Neil sat on his father's shoulders watching aircraft zoom across the sky. His eyes tracked the wings overhead. Neil left the races holding tight to his first model airplane and to the spark that lit his childhood.

The next summer Stephen and Viola Armstrong gave Neil a baby sister. Neil put on air shows for June, but he decided he needed more planes to keep her entertained.

Dad helped Neil make his first paper airplane. Dad folded, and Neil creased the edges until the plane was ready to launch. It made trip after trip.

June giggled every time it soared overhead. When the plane was too bent and battered for another flight, Mom pressed out the paper, and Neil folded it all by himself.

At Grandpa Engel's farm Neil gathered straw and bits of wood. He bent, twisted, and glued the pieces together till he had three new models to test.

Neil shouted to his family, "Come one! Come all to the Armstrong Air Show!"

Grandma and Grandpa cheered for each flight, and they hugged him after each crash. Neil returned home with a basket of building material and three new airplanes.

Dad kept Neil supplied with paper. One day he brought home a few rubber bands. "Put one end here. Now twist. Ready, set, let go!" The plane soared across the room.

"My planes have never gone so far, so fast. Thanks, Dad!" Neil spent hours testing his new power supply. He could barely stop for dinner.

Neil made model after model. They zoomed through the house, but in February of 1935 Neil learned to make quieter planes. He didn't want to wake his new baby brother. Neil thundered through his loudest flights when Dean was awake and could join in.

Neil climbed aboard his first 'real' airplane on the way to Sunday School. Dad spotted a sign advertising rides aboard The Tin Goose.

Neil read the billboard, "8AM, twenty-five cents a ride. 12 Noon, fifty cents." Neil sighed, no ride today. By the time Sunday School was over, plane rides would be too expensive.

Dad drove into the parking lot. "Let's skip Sunday School, but don't tell Mom or June. It's our little secret."

Neil leaped out of the car. "Don't worry, Dad. Six-year-olds don't tattle." By the time the Tin Goose landed, Neil had locked away his secret. He wanted another ride.

Neil started first grade a few weeks later. He loved reading signs and hearing stories, but now he wanted to read his own books. By the end of the year, he'd devoured over a hundred.

In second grade Mrs. Adams called Neil's parents in for a conference. "Take a look. Here's what my class is reading, and Neil just finished this fifth-grade book. He should go to third grade now, not at the end of the year."

Neil's parents agreed. The following Monday Neil started third grade, and he blossomed. By fourth grade his teacher had two problems . . . she didn't have enough books to keep Neil busy, and paper planes weren't allowed in school.

Neil discovered balsa wood when he was ten. His cousin Kenneth gave him a boxful, and Neil couldn't go back to scraps. Balsa was easy to cut and shape the way he imagined, but he'd have to buy it. Neil needed a job.

Dad heard the cemetery was hiring someone to mow grass. Neil wasn't worried about ghosts. He was the boy for the job. Neil earned ten cents an hour, enough to keep him supplied with balsa wood. Enough to save up for store-bought models and kits.

Over the years Neil built a squadron of his own. Big planes, little planes. Models that flew across his room or nosedived into the ground. Several looked like the Tin Goose. A few could have come from air shows.

Neil hung them from his bedroom ceiling. They filled his room and spread across a corner in the basement.

Neil didn't tell his parents how he made room for more. He launched the old ones out the upstairs window.

He set some on fire and studied their smoky trip to the ground. He wrote down his results, sketched new designs, and created planes that flew farther across the yard.

Neil kept on reading. He discovered aviation magazines in middle school. He searched the pages for articles on engineers and their wind tunnel experiments.

He recorded their results in his notebooks. He wanted to be the engineer who sent wind blasting down tunnels, the one who used the results to build better planes.

Neil was almost sixteen, but the spark from that long-ago race was burning bright.

CHAPTER 2

A Summer's Dream

On the first day of summer vacation Neil started building his senior physics project, a wind tunnel.

Notebooks covered his desk and sat stacked against his bedroom walls, each page crammed with research. Diagrams showed how to power the wind. Tables noted the details of each plane, flaws and advantages. Charts calculated lift and drag on the wings.

Neil sifted through his notebooks, searching for the perfect wind tunnel. He rejected each one. They couldn't compete with the Wright Brothers' design. It helped them build the first successful flying machine.

Neil picked the Wright Brothers to be his teachers. He studied his notebook page about them, and then he made a list . . . stovepipe for the tunnel, an electric motor to power the wind, a rheostat to control air speed, and blades big enough to send Neil's dream airborne.

Neil and his brother Dean scoured the junkyard all summer. They found miles of stovepipe but nothing powerful enough to create gale-force winds.

Dean spotted four fan blades. "Come on, Neil. You can use them till you find something better."

Neil said, "Something that small would be a waste of time, but if you want them, they're yours." The brothers strapped the blades to their bikes and pedaled home.

The month of June passed into July, but Neil refused to worry. He still had a month to look for supplies. If he couldn't find what he needed, he'd buy it.

His drug store job, sweeping floors and stocking shelves, paid forty cents an hour. Neil scrimped and saved every penny for his wind tunnel. And for flying lessons.

Very few aeronautical engineers piloted planes. They believed in studying wind tunnels, but Neil remembered the flight aboard the Tin Goose with his dad.

Being inside a real plane with wind rushing past was different than peeking inside a wind tunnel and watching air hit a tiny model. He wanted to do both.

Neil knew he needed to fly if he wanted to design great aircraft. The Wright Brothers piloted their own planes, and he would too.

It was expensive, nine dollars a lesson, but Neil thought it was worth the price. He spent the summer working at the drug store, scouring the junkyard, and riding his bike out to the grassy airfield outside town.

Neil turned 16 on August 5, 1946. He didn't take his driver's test. He'd never bothered with cars, but Neil took lessons from three veteran pilots all summer-long. Frank Lucie, Aubrey Knudegaard, and Charles Finkenbine drilled Neil like he was an army pilot under their command.

A few days after his birthday, Frank gave him the okay for his solo flight. "Take it up, Neil. I'll watch from the ground."

"Yes, sir!" Neil scrambled aboard, but he felt like he was moving in slow motion.

"You're ready, Neil. Show me you paid attention during lessons." Frank spun the propellers till the plane started.

Neil swallowed the lump in his throat and headed down the runway. He was alone in the cockpit for the very first time.

Neil focused on breathing in, then breathing out. He let his training take over as he soared skyward and looped around the airport. Neil's face lit up as he touched down and climbed out.

Frank slapped him on the back. "Congratulations! You just earned your pilot's license. I'll buy you a pop to celebrate!"

Neil spent the dwindling days of August shopping. He bought his motor and ordered the rheostat at the hardware store, but he still couldn't find a propeller.

Neil called the salvage and army surplus stores in Dayton and Columbus. Nothing. He left his phone number. Each time he'd wait a few days before calling back. Still nothing.

It was almost time for school to start. "Don't worry, Neil," said Dean. "Start small with my fan blades. They'll help you work out the glitches."

"Thanks, but I'll give it one last try." Neil made another round of calls. Nothing again. He dialed the last number, but he couldn't believe his ears, "Yes, sir. We have a propeller, but it's reserved for a young man from Wapakoneta. Sorry."

Neil shouted, "I'm that young man!"

Neil watched and waited for Dad to pull in the driveway. He jumped in before Dad could switch off the motor. They were off to pick up the propeller before it flew away.

He carried it downstairs to the basement and put it with his other supplies . . . the electric motor, the rheostat, and lots of stove pipe.

Neil couldn't wait to put the pieces together. It felt like doing a giant jigsaw puzzle, and that's when Neil discovered a problem. The axle on the motor was too small to hold the propeller in place. It could spin off into space, slashing anything it touched.

CHAPTER 3
Building a Wind Tunnel

Neil made another trip to the junkyard looking for a way to solve his deadly new problem.

He found an old metal adapter that fit between the motor and propeller, but he still couldn't put them together. He couldn't punch holes into the propeller hub at home, but he could in the school workshop. It had the right tools.

Neil made himself wait, until he found another project. He wired the motor and rheostat together. At least they were ready.

The first day of school arrived, and Neil couldn't wait any longer. He went in early to talk to Mr. Crites. His physics teacher told him to leave the parts in the workshop. Then

Mr. Crites promised to meet him the next day after school.

Mr. Crites helped Neil punch holes in the adapter, line them up to the propeller, and bolt the pieces together. "This looks great! I bet the Wright Brothers would get a kick out of seeing a high school kid recreate their wind tunnel."

Neil carried the new part home to his basement. He pushed the adapter onto the axle and clamped them together. He spun the propeller with one hand. Nothing flip-flopped loose, but would a motor send the propeller blades flying?

Neil set the rheostat on low, plugged in the motor, and flipped the power switch. The motor whirred to life. The propeller twirled but remained in place.

"Yes!" cheered Neil.

POP! The motor died, and the basement went black.

Mom hollered downstairs, "Neil, you blew a fuse! Change it now! I can't see to start dinner!"

Neil turned on his flashlight and unplugged the motor. His hypothesis — the engine took too much power away from the basement's electrical circuit. That melted the fuse and stopped the electricity.

Upstairs the kitchen lights went out. They must be on the same electrical track. No circuit, no motor, no lights in the kitchen or basement.

Neil swapped out the old fuse. He hoped the new one was stronger. Otherwise he'd spend all day changing them. Neil decided to save up for more fuses. He crossed his fingers, plugged in the motor, and flipped the switch.

The motor purred to life and spun the propeller in a slow circle. A gentle breeze tugged on the basement squadron that hung from the ceiling.

Neil cheered as the wind rocked his models back and forth. He switched off the motor, and the planes returned to their hangars. Time for a little more speed!

Neil dialed the rheostat to medium. He turned on the power. *POP* went the fuse as the circuit blew open, and the basement went black again.

June called downstairs, "Change that fuse! I can't see to mash the potatoes!"

A light appeared at the top of the stairs. It was Dean and a flashlight. "Mom sent me down to help."

Neil called, "I could use an extra set of hands."

Dean hurried downstairs and focused his light on the fuse. Neil changed it and flipped the switch. The basement lights came on, and the propeller spun to life. His planes sailed round and round from their overhead hangars.

Neil's thoughts swirled with them. Did he dare turn the rheostat to high? Could his planes handle more wind? Could the fuses?

CHAPTER 4

Keeping Current

Neil set the rheostat on high and flipped the switch. The motor roared to life. Gale force winds blasted the basement squadron. The planes dove, twisted, and crashed into each other. Neil cheered, till he heard *POP*, and the basement went dark, again.

Dean flipped on his flashlight and pointed it at the fuse. "See! I can help."

Mom called down, "Fix that fuse, or you'll be eating lumpy gravy! I can't see what I'm stirring.'"

Neil swapped out the fuse and stared at his mess of a squadron. "Hey Dean, would you untangle those planes?"

"Sure." Dean reached for the nearest clump.

Neil headed upstairs. He wondered how he'd explain fuses to his mother.

"Neil Alden Armstrong, are you so hungry you're snacking on fuses before dinner?"

"No," groaned Neil. "I'm trying to make my propeller spin at different speeds, but it takes so much electricity that I'm melting fuses and shutting down lights! The kitchen and basement must be on the same circuit.

"Could I move those kitchen plugs to a dining room outlet? That should put them on a different electrical circle."

Mom glanced around the kitchen. "Sorry, I can't move them or anything else. Take a break till dinner's over. I'll be done in the kitchen, and you can have the electricity downstairs.

Neil sighed. "How can I help? I want to get back to work."

Mom said, "Have Dean set the table. You stir the gravy."

The brothers went to work to get dinner ready. They wolfed it down.

Mom and the kids worked as a team on dishes so the boys could have all the electricity downstairs.

Neil started the motor. Wind battered the planes, but the lights stayed on. Problem solved! He'd work on the wind tunnel when Mom was out of the kitchen.

Neil turned off the power and helped Dean pull the planes apart. As they worked, Neil scanned the stovepipe for his first section of wind tunnel. It needed to be short and propeller-wide.

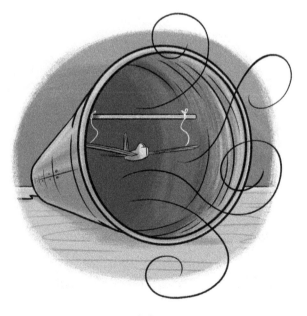

Neil found the perfect piece. He set it on the table, centered it around the propeller blade, and laid his model inside. This could work, but he still had to anchor everything so it wouldn't blow away.

The stovepipe was easy. Dean grabbed a couple of clamps from Dad's workshop. He clipped the stovepipe and table together.

The plane was trickier. It had to rise and fall with the wind but not fly away. Neil pictured several ways to secure it. He decided to put a rod across the tunnel. He'd tie the wings to the rod.

The brothers searched the pile of stovepipe for a narrow cylinder. It had to be a little longer than the propeller. Neil grabbed a rod that looked about right and held it up against his new tunnel. It was a couple inches longer than he needed, but it would work.

Dean got the drill, and Neil found a rod-size bit. He bored a hole into the left side of his new wind tunnel and slid the cylinder all the way to the right. Perfect! Neil banged the rod against the metal till Dean noticed a dent. "Hey, let me drill this hole."

"What would Dad say?"

"That I'm too young," said Dean. "Okay, you drill, but I'm in charge of the rod."

Neil punched another hole through the metal. Dean slid the rod across the width of the tunnel, and Neil tied the wings in place.

"Time for a test." Neil set the rheostat on low and switched on the motor. The propeller made a lazy circle. The breeze fluttered and lifted the plane. Success!

Dean cheered.

Neil moved the knob to medium. His model climbed higher.

Dean called, "Faster!"

Neil turned the knob again. Wind blasted down the tunnel, his plane strained against its tethers, and the basement squadron began maneuvers. They dove, twisted, and crashed into each other. Success!

Dean groaned. "More planes to untangle."

CHAPTER 5

Experimenting with Trouble

Neil switched off the power. "Hey Dean! Get Mom!"

Dean raced upstairs. Neil listened for footsteps before turning on the motor.

Wind blasted out of the tunnel and up the stairs. It flattened Dean's hair. It snatched the robe off Mom's shoulders and threw it at the ceiling.

Neil laughed, till his model broke free. It blew across the room *SMASH-CRASH* into the window.

Dean snorted at the broken glass. "Anything you want to buy?"

"But it worked!"

"Yeah, it was a smash-hit!" laughed Dean.

Mom marched down the stairs and over to the window. "Neil Alden Armstrong, I expect you to clean up this mess *and* pay for a new window."

"But Mom..."

"Don't but-Mom me! I know this is a school project, but if you can pay for all those flying lessons, you can pay for this too. Now find a broom, and start sweeping."

Mom grabbed her robe. "It's bedtime, and I'd better not see this mess tomorrow morning."

***

At school Neil shared his windy results with his physics class. Everyone laughed about the broken window, everyone except Neil.

Mr. Crites said, "It looks like having a horizontal rod running across the tunnel was the problem. Too much thrust from those propellers yanked the plane loose.

"Let me see if I have something to help you." He pulled a thin metal rod and a couple of rubber stoppers out of a cabinet.

Mr. Crites said, "Slide the rod vertically through your plane. It will make a tiny hole. Then slide a stopper above and below the model to make it more secure. It will also make it easier to measure lift."

Then Mr. Crites pulled out a spring scale. It had a hook on the top and the bottom, and a weight scale in the middle.

"That looks like the scale my dad uses to weigh fish," said Neil.

"They work the same," said Mr. Crites. "Hook this to the top of the plane and the top of the tunnel to measure your lift. Let the tunnel be your teacher. Test it by using different models, in different positions, at different speeds."

"Yes, sir," said Neil. "Anything else?"

Mr. Crites laughed. "Of course! Try the new set-up tonight. Record your results in your science journal. Compare and contrast the old equipment with your new gear. Be ready to share in class tomorrow."

"Yes, sir!"

Neil brought in his journal the next day, each time he tried something new, or whenever Mr. Crites was teaching aerodynamics.

By the end of the year Neil finished his third notebook, added more stovepipe to his tunnel, and tested the new aerodynamic theories he'd learned. The tunnel stretched the length of the basement.

Neil still found time to fly. He logged twenty hours in the sky his senior year. The best part, without an instructor the price was only seven dollars. A real bargain, but Neil found a better one.

The airport mechanic needed someone to slow time the planes after he overhauled the engines. Neil volunteered. He wanted to understand planes from the inside out.

The mechanic idled the motor first. Neil helped him search for oil leaks and engine stress. If they didn't find any, they sped up to low. If everything still looked good, Neil flew the airplane at top speed for fifteen minutes before bringing it in for a final check.

The best part — if the engine remained stress-free, Neil could zoom across the sky for another hour, sometimes two. Nothing was better than overhauling a plane and getting free time in the sky.

Neil finally took time to learn to drive that spring. He got his license just in time to take his best friend and their dates to prom.

CHAPTER 6
Graduation and Beyond

Neil Alden Armstrong stepped forward to accept a handshake and a diploma from the Superintendent of Wapakoneta Schools.

He was still sixteen, but the youngest graduate of Blume High School's class of 1947 had a secret. He'd already taken a giant step towards his future.

By midsummer, Neil got the letter he'd been waiting for. He breathed a sigh of relief when he read the first word, congratulations. He'd won a Holloway scholarship thanks to his studies, the wind tunnel experiments, and his flight time.

His dreams were ready for take-off, and now it was time to tell Mom. Neil found her in the basement examining her preserves. "Mom! Mom!"

Viola startled. The jar of blackberries slipped from her fingers and shattered on her foot. Juice, berries, and glass splattered everywhere.

Neil helped her to a clean spot. Then he started wiping up the mess. "Mom, I've got great news. I'm going to college. Free! At

Purdue University! I won a Holloway scholarship! Now I can major in aeronautical engineering and study airplane design."

Mom said, "Free college! That's great!"

"And I'll get a chance to fly Navy fighter jets."

"Fighter jets," squeaked Mom. She didn't say another word till Neil parked the car at the doctor's office. The diagnoses - broken foot, stressed-out Mom.

Viola was relieved to learn Neil would spend the next two years studying aeronautical engineering on the ground at Purdue. He wouldn't have much time to fly.

Neil was busy six days a week with school, in class three hours each morning. In science labs three hours every afternoon, but he felt himself growing, becoming an engineer.

At age eighteen the Navy launched him into the cockpit of a fighter jet. He flew seventy-eight missions over Korea, and he logged 121 hours in the air. A lot had changed for Neil since he left Wapakoneta.

Neil resigned from active duty in 1952, but he stayed in the Navy Reserves so he could keep flying. He wanted to get back to Purdue, his Holloway scholarship, and an aeronautical engineering career.

Once more Neil studied six days a week, six hours a day. He graduated three years later.

Neil couldn't leave technology behind so he found a job as a research test pilot. His first assignment . . . to pilot a chase plane.

He'd follow the modified bombers until they dropped the rockets and jets from their wings and bellies. Neil chased after them shooting camera footage and watching for signs of engine stress. He loved his job!

Neil spent the next seven years flying everything from jets and rockets to helicopters and gliders. In 1962 Neil waited for a new letter. Seven pilot engineers would fly into space. He cheered when he found his name on the list.

Neil entered the astronaut training program. He studied zero gravity and practiced working in a space suit, but he also studied the Saturn rocket and its engines. Neil blasted into outer space in March of 1966.

Gemini Eight was supposed to orbit the earth for seventy-five hours. Eleven hours in, his ship was spinning out-of-control, and Neil was close to passing out.

He shut down the engine and turned on the backward thrusters. It stopped the spin, but he'd used three-fourths of the fuel. There was no choice. Gemini Eight returned to Earth immediately.

In September of that same year Neil prepared for the launch of Gemini Eleven. He was the back-up commander, ready to climb aboard or help from the ground. After Gemini Eight he was glad there were no unexpected problems.

Neil and every single NASA astronaut dreamed about flying aboard Apollo Eleven. It would be the first spaceship to land on the moon.

In December of 1968 Neil not only earned a seat. He was named mission commander and would get to make the first moon walk.

On July 20, 1969 Neil stepped onto the lunar surface and into history. He got two hours and fifteen minutes to take pictures and collect moon rock samples.

He also took time to hop, skip, and jump before planting the American flag and talking to the president.

Neil's teen-age dream to build a wind tunnel had taken him to the moon, and it brought him safely back home again.

Author's Note

I was ten when Neil landed on the moon. The best part . . . I got to stay up past midnight to watch him take that first step. His parents lived around the block from me. Neil was part of my childhood, and now he's the hero of my first book.

I still live in Wapakoneta, and I volunteer at the Armstrong Air and Space Museum. In early 2018 I saw a remnant of the original wind tunnel, and I was fascinated to discover it was Neil's senior physics project. He was only sixteen.

In March of 2018 Wapakoneta was a year out from the fiftieth anniversary of the moon landing, and the town was making plans for the big event. I was taking a writing class, and Neil's story kept popping into my head.

In May I gave in and started researching Neil. I checked out books from the library. I googled websites.

I asked the director at the Armstrong museum for help. She sent me a NASA link. After all that searching I found three details about the wind tunnel. That was it!

1. Neil used stovepipe, a motor, a rheostat, and a propeller to build it. Neil and Dean found the stovepipe at the junkyard.

2. Neil blew a lot of fuses when he added in the rheostat.

3. He used his wind tunnel to send Mom's robe flying. That's also when he broke the basement window.

In 1947 Neil left the wind tunnel and Wapakoneta behind when he went off to Purdue. He didn't travel to the moon until 1969, and the wind tunnel was forgotten, except for those three details.

I wish I could ask Neil for the missing facts, but he died August 25, 2012. I would have asked Neil about his wind tunnel.

Instead I used my research to imagine how it worked. I drew conclusions to put the information back together. I invented scenes and dialogue to bring the story back to life once more. It was like doing the most challenging puzzle, with 1946 technology.

Whenever I read historical fiction, I always wonder what's true and what the author had to invent. Read the back matter to discover the truth behind my story, *Neil Armstrong's Wind Tunnel Dream.*

PART 1

What's true

Chapter 1

* Neil went to the 1932 air races in Cleveland, Ohio. He was two years old.

* He built his first planes out of paper, straw, and scraps of wood. He powered them with rubber bands.

* He skipped Sunday School to ride the Tin Goose when he was six. It cost twenty-five cents to ride the Ford Trimotor plane in the morning, more later in the day.

* Neil started school as a first grader and read over 100 books that year.

* Mrs. Adams, Neil's second-grade teacher, discovered him reading at a fourth/fifth grade level. She called the superintendent who moved Neil up to third grade.

* Neil did well in third grade with Mrs. Schrolucke. Miss Oelrich, his fourth-grade teacher said she "couldn't keep him busy all the time." Neil flew through his classwork.

* At age ten Neil got his first job cutting grass at the Old Mission Cemetery in Upper Sandusky. He made ten cents an hour.

* His cousin Kenneth Benzine introduced Neil to balsa wood between age eight and age ten.

* Neil had planes hanging from his bedroom ceiling. They filled a corner of the basement too.

* In his early teens he read aviation magazines. Neil used a notebook to record

technical information for each plane he read about.

* Neil launched planes out a second-floor window to watch them crash. Sometimes he even set them on fire.

Chapter 2

* Neil built a wind tunnel for his senior physics project for Mr. Crites.

* Neil modeled his wind tunnel after the Wright Brothers' design.

* Neil and his brother Dean went to the junkyard looking for a motor, rheostat, propeller, and stovepipe. They found only stovepipe.

* Dean found some fan blades. He brought them home, but Neil still used a propeller.

* Neil worked at Rhine and Brading Drug store after school and during the summer. He

swept floors and stocked shelves for forty cents an hour.

* Neil took flight lessons during the summer of 1946 for nine dollars a lesson. His three teachers, Frank Lucie, Aubrey Knudegaard, and Charles Finkenbine, were veteran army pilots.

* Neil got his pilot's license a few days after his sixteenth birthday. Frank Lucie was his instructor. Aubrey told a friend to stick around for a Coke because there might be something to celebrate, like Neil getting his license.

Chapter 3
* Neil blew a lot of fuses trying to put in the rheostat.

Chapter 4
* Setting the rheostat at different speeds blew more fuses.

Chapter 5

* Neil sent Dean to get their mother when the wind tunnel was done. Neil aimed the wind at the bottom step. He turned it on and blew off her housecoat. He also blew out a basement window. Neil thought it was funny. Mom didn't.

* After Neil earned his pilot's license, he logged twenty hours in a plane by the end of the school year. Neil said he "built up flight time, by doing slow time after top cylinder overhauls." He flew the small airplanes first on low, then on high to make sure the engine worked properly after the overhaul.

Chapter 6

* Neil graduated high school at age sixteen. He earned the Holloway Scholarship to study engineering at Purdue and to fly fighter jets for the Navy.

* Neil startled Mom when she was in the basement looking for a jar of fruit for a pie.

She dropped the jar on her foot and broke both the jar and her foot. Neil cleaned up the mess and told Mom about his college scholarship.

* Neil went to school six days a week, six hours a day. He spent three hours in class, three hours in a lab.

* His first job was as an experimental research test pilot. He got to chase down and film the rockets or jets that were launched from a modified bomber.

* Neil was selected to join the NASA astronaut corps in 1962.

* He commanded Gemini Eight in 1966. The ship was spinning out-of-control. He and David Scott were close to passing out. Neil stopped the spin, saving the ship and their lives.

* He was the back-up commander for Gemini Eleven.

* Neil stepped onto the moon July 20, 1969.

*
*   *
*

PART 2

How to Build a Tunnel for Wind, Primary Version

Here's what you need:

Clear tube   Table-top fan

A tunnel for the wind doesn't need to be complicated. A fan and a clear tube will work. I recommend finding a tube that's 8-10 inches in diameter and 3-4 feet long. It will give you the best view of the wind at work. Set the fan next to your tube, and you have a starter tunnel.

Here are some things to test-fly: tissues, beanie babies, handkerchiefs, packing peanuts, paper cups . . . anything soft that will fly safely. Also please stay safe by keeping fingers and all objects out of the fan.

***

Here are some things to think about and try:

* How does the tunnel of wind work?

* How can you make the wind blow faster? Slower?

* What goes up the tube? What doesn't? What makes the difference?

* What can float? What will sink? Why?

* If you change the angle of the tunnel, what happens? Did anything stay the same? Did anything change?

***

Do you ever watch the effects of wind outside? Inside you can turn it on and off with the tunnel of wind. You can control its speed. Here are some things to try:

* Watch the wind outside. Can you make it do the same things inside your tunnel?

* What happens to water when wind blows across it? Try wetting the end of the tube. Make the fan go fast. What happened to the water? Try this again and make the fan go slow. What was the same? What was different?

* Repeat the water experiment, this time with a bowl of water near the end of the tube. Did you get the same results, or did something change?

* What does the tunnel of wind inside teach you about wind direction outside?

* What other wind experiments can you do inside, now that you control the wind?

***

Start a journal, and write entries about what you see. You'll be just like Neil. If you get stuck, here are some starter sentences . . .

* I predict . . .

* This happened . . .

* I learned . . .

Activity Source:

https://www.youtube.com/watch?v=JjpeRG
xdizQ

The tunnel in this video is attached to a lever. It allows you to lift and lower the tube so you can change the angle of the tunnel.

It isn't a true wind tunnel because it's missing the funnel and the plenum. You can build them in the more advanced version in Part 3. Also, a true wind tunnel is designed to measure the lift a plane gets from the wind.

PART 3

How to Build a Wind Tunnel Advanced Version

Figure 1

This is my wind tunnel. It looks a lot like Neil's tunnel, and it would make a great science fair project. It would only take a couple hours to make if you have a parent helping you. It was big enough I could test a foam glider inside it. I modeled it after a link I found online.

Figure 2

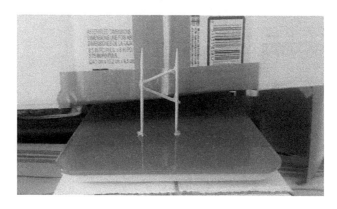

Figure 3

Here's what I used:
- Table-top Fan (or box fan)
- Small digital kitchen scale
- Tape Measure
- 2 Clear sheets of acetate
- Glue gun/sticks or Craft Glue

- Duct tape

- Three small cardboard boxes

(4 x 9.5 x 6.25)

- One medium box

(14 x 10 x 6.25)

- 11 Craft tubes or cylinders 1 yard long

(paper/cardboard/plastic)

Cut into 12-inch lengths.

You can find these supplies at stores like Walmart, Meijer, or Target.

Directions:

1. Duct tape the 4 sides of the small cardboard boxes to make them sturdy. Tape the ends together to make one long tunnel. *Figure 1.*

2. Cut your tubes into foot-long lengths. A parent can help you with this. Fit them inside the box until it's full. This will help you to pull them out and glue them back into place. This part of the tunnel is called the plenum or diffuser. It straightens the wind. *Figure 2*

3. Duct tape the 4 sides of the medium box to make the funnel. Tape one end to the fan, the other end to the plenum. *Figure 1*

4. Cut a window a couple inches past the end of the tubes. Cut another one into the side of the tunnel just below the first window. Duct tape the edges for both windows. Measure the acetate against each window. Cut each piece a little larger than its window. Lay them over the opening and duct tape them in place. *Figure 1*

5. Cut a 3-inch slot below the window. Match your digital kitchen scale to this spot, and put 2 dots of hot glue an inch apart on the scale. Hold a toothpick on each dot until dry. Glue 2 more toothpicks between them in the shape of a V. It will give the base more support. *Figure 3*

6. When the base is solid, slide the toothpicks and scale into position. If your wind tunnel isn't level, set books or cardboard underneath it. *Figure 1*

7. Slide your model onto the toothpick base. Now you're ready to test your wind tunnel. *Figure 1*

This source helped me build my wind tunnel.

https://www.instructables.com/id/Cardboard-Wind-Tunnel/

$*$ $*$
$*$ $*$

PART 4

Let's use your wind tunnel!

1. Check your scale. Record the reading. Don't be surprised if it's 0. (Mine was.)

2. Make a prediction – what do you think will happen when you turn on the fan?

3. Switch on the power. What happened to your reading? (Mine went into negative numbers. That's lift at work!)

Keep exploring:

1. Try the fan at different speeds. Did the scale change? How?

2. Try planes made with different materials. Change the wings. Try omitting parts of the plane like the wing or the rudder. Your goal - how low can the scale go? The lower the number, the more lift you're getting.

You can go much farther with wind tunnels. Google them online, and you'll find more experiments and ideas to test out. Happy Experimenting!

Bibliography

* Byars, Ann. Neil Armstrong: The First Man on the Moon. New York: Rosen, 2004

* Editors, THEFAMOUSPEOPLE "Neil Armstrong Biography." *THEFAMOUSPEOPLE*. 21 July 2017. 21 May 2018. <https://www.thefamouspeople.com/profiles/neil-alden-armstrong-2430.php>

* Hansen, James R. First Man: The Life of Neil A. Armstrong. New York: Simon & Schuster, 2005

* Goalieguy. "Cardboard Wind Tunnel." *Instructables*. <https://www.instructables.com/id/Cardboard-Wind-Tunnel/>

* KodoKids. "Wind Tunnel Science Activity for Kids – Experiment and Hypothesize." <https://www.youtube.com/watch?v=JjpeRGxdizQ>

* NASA Johnson Space Center Oral History Project. "Oral History Transcript Neil A. Armstrong Interviewed by Dr. Stephen E. Ambrose and Dr. Douglas Brinkley Houston, Texas." 19 September 2001. 21 May 2018. <https://www.nasa.gov/pdf/62281main_armstrong_oralhistory.pdf>.

* Paur, Jason. "The Aircraft and Spacecraft of Neil Armstrong's Career." *Gear*. 29 August 2012. 21 May 2018 <https://www.wired.com/2012/08/neil-armstrong-aircraft/>

* Wagner, Leon. One Giant Leap: Neil Armstrong's Stellar American Journey. New York: Forge, 2004

* Wendell, Bryan. "Neil Armstrong's success in space didn't surprise his fellow Boy

Scouts." *Bryan On Scouting.* 20 July 2016. 21 May   2018. <https://blog.scoutingmagazine.org/2016/0 7/20/neil-armstrongs-success-space-didnt-surprise-fellow-boy-scouts/>

Other Sources:

* Collins, Michael. "Michael Collins: The Neil Armstrong I knew – and flew with." *The Washington Post.* 12 September 2012. 21 May 2018.<https://www.washingtonpost.com/o pinions/michael-collins-the-neil-armstrong-i-knew--and-flew-with/2012/09/12/b3f7556c-fb7c-11e1-8adc-499661af>

* Neil Armstrong Biography." *Encyclopedia of World Biographies.* 21 May 2018. <http://www.notablebiographies.com/An-Ba/Armstrong-Neil.html#ixzz5HaNyW3Yv>

* Neil Armstrong facts for kids." *Kids Encyclopedia Facts*. 21 May 2018. <https://kids.kiddle.co/Neil_Armstrong>

* "10 Facts about Neil Armstrong." 21 May 2018. <http://celebritylook3.info/10-facts-about-neil-armstrong/2/>

Acknowledgements

Thanks to the staff and volunteers at the Armstrong Air and Space Museum. Without them, there would be no story.

My critique friends told me what was good and what didn't work. Thanks to Debbie, Rick, Donna, Charlotte, Carolyn K, Carolyn C, Alex, Mira, Callie, Melissa, Candice, Candace, Sandra, Theresa, Nancy, Patricia, Karen, and Shirin. They're my writing community.

A special thank you to Donna and Cole. Donna was my guide and guru to self-publishing. Cole took on Neil and I late in November, and he did it beautifully.

Finally, I want to thank my husband Wayne. He helped me picture all things electrical. Without his help, I couldn't have put the wind tunnel back together again.

ABOUT THE AUTHOR

Rinda never planned to write. She was a second-grade teacher who read and told stories, until the night a bat paid her a visit. It inspired her to write. She learned how to edit, thanks to SCBWI, writing classes, and critique partners. Rinda substitute teaches to stay connected to today's kids. She uses her knowledge and imagination to write stories for them. Her website features a weekly blog and book review for kids. She expanded her career to open a company, Beach Girl Press. Visit Rinda at www.rindabeach.com

Cole Roberts is an Illustrator based in Nashville, Tennessee who loves creating artwork for children's publications. You can find more of his work by visiting www.coleswork.com